Why Should I?

Written by Sue Graves

Illustrated by
Emanuela Carletti and
Desideria Guicciardini

W

FRANKLIN WATTS
LONDON • SYDNEY

Arin didn't look after **anything**.
He didn't look after his toys.
He broke them all the time.

"You need to **respect** your toys," said Dad.

Arin didn't look after his clothes.
He **never bothered** to hang them
up or put them away in the right place.

"You need to respect your clothes," said Mum.

If anyone asked him to be more respectful, he just muttered,

"Why should I?"

Arin didn't respect other people's belongings either. When he wanted to play with Anish's pirate ship, he just **took it**. He didn't even ask first. Worse still, he broke the sails on it.

Anish was upset.
He said Arin should show more respect
for **other people's things**.

Later, Arin wanted to borrow a book from Vanna. He ignored the "DO NOT ENTER" sign on her door and just **walked in.**

Vanna was cross. She said
he should show more respect for
other people's space!

At school, Arin saw his best friend Junior. Junior told him that he was going to watch his first skateboarding competition. He said he was **very excited**.

But Arin laughed at him and said he thought skateboarding was silly. Junior was upset. He said Arin was **being rude**. He said Arin should **respect other people's opinions** and not laugh at them!

At playtime, Arin played with his football. But he kept kicking it into the class garden. The ball knocked over everyone's pots and the plants spilled everywhere. **Everyone was cross** with him. They told Mr Counter.

Mr Counter said Arin should
think about his behaviour
when he got home.

Arin was upset. He **didn't mean** to make people cross. He especially **didn't mean** to make Junior sad. He went to talk to Grandma.

Arin asked Grandma why people were cross and sad. Grandma said people wanted to be treated respectfully. Grandma asked Arin **how he would feel** if someone broke his things or laughed at things he liked.

Arin had a think. He said he wouldn't like it at all! **He was sorry** that he hadn't treated people the way he would like to be treated. He said he would **try hard** to be more respectful in future.

19

The next day, Arin played more carefully with his toys. He hung up his clothes, too.

Arin asked Anish **first** if he could play with his racing car.

He knocked on Vanna's door **first** before going into her room.

He said **sorry** to Junior for not respecting his opinions. He **listened politely** while Junior told the class about the skateboarding competition. He said it sounded really good fun.

Then Arin said **SORRY** to everyone in the class for knocking over their plants. He helped them plant them again. Everyone **was pleased** with Arin for being more respectful.

Arin noticed that everyone **treated him better** because he showed more respect. He said being respectful was much nicer.

Can you tell the story of what happens when Milly throws her ball against her neighbour's wall?

How do you think her neighbour felt in the first picture? How does Milly feel at the end?

A note about sharing this book

The *Our Emotions and Behaviour* series has been developed to provide a starting point for further discussion on children's feelings and behaviour, both in relation to themselves and to other people.

Why Should I?
This book looks in a reassuring way at why it is important to have respect, not only for ourselves and our own things but for other people and their possessions, too.

The book aims to encourage children to have a developing awareness of behavioural expectations in different settings. It also invites children to begin to consider the consequences of their words and actions for themselves and others.

Storyboard puzzle
The wordless storyboard on pages 26 and 27 provides an opportunity for speaking and listening. Children are encouraged to tell the story illustrated in the panels: Milly is throwing her ball against her neighbour's wall and making dirty marks. When the neighbour talks to her about it, Milly stops and cleans the wall. She ends up playing ball with her neighbour's son instead.

How to use the book
The book is designed for adults to share with either an individual child, or a group of children, and as a starting point for discussion.

The book also provides visual support and repeated words and phrases to build confidence in children who are starting to read on their own.

Before reading the story
Choose a time to read when you and the children are relaxed and have time to share the story.

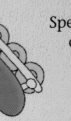

Spend time looking at the illustrations and talk about what the book may be about before reading it together.

After reading, talk about the book with the children:

- What was the book about? Have the children ever been careless with toys or their clothes? What were the consequences if they did not look after their things? Invite the children to talk about their experiences.
- Have they ever experienced someone not respecting them or their possessions? How did it make them feel?
- As a group, talk about why it is important to treat others as they themselves would wish to be treated. Encourage the children to take turns to speak and to listen politely while others are talking.
- Look at the storyboard puzzle and talk about what is happening in the story. Invite children to play out the storyboard. Discuss performances afterwards as a group.

Talk about being part of a school family. Why is it important to show respect to others in school? What examples can they give? Examples may be standing patiently and quietly in a queue; not interrupting when others are speaking; not pushing past others; asking first if you want to borrow something; taking care with other people's possessions; being respectful of other people's opinions. Make a list of these examples and display them.

To Isabelle, William A, George, William G, Max, Emily,
Leo, Caspar, Felix and Phoebe –S.G.

Franklin Watts
Published in paperback in Great Britain in 2020 by The Watts Publishing Group

Text © The Watts Publishing Group 2019
Illustrations © Emanuela Carletti and Desideria Guicciardini 2019

ISBN 978 1 4451 6566 0

Editor: Jackie Hamley
Designer: Peter Scoulding

Printed in China

FSC
www.fsc.org
MIX
Paper from
responsible sources
FSC® C104740

Franklin Watts
An imprint of
Hachette Children's Group
Part of The Watts Publishing Group
Carmelite House
50 Victoria Embankment
London EC4Y 0DZ

An Hachette UK Company
www.hachette.co.uk

www.franklinwatts.co.uk